11+
MATHS
Short Tests
Levels 3-6

Testbook 1

Stephen C. Curran

edited by Tandip Mann,
Anne-Marie Choong
& Andrea Richardson

This book belongs to:

....

_____

Accelerated Education Publications Ltd

Do your workings on this page

Mark to %	
0	0%
1	7%
2	13%
3	20%
4	27%
5	33%
6	40%
7	47%
8	53%
9	60%
10	67%
11	73%
12	80%
13	87%
14	93%
15	100%

Maths Test 1

1) Find the sum of the even numbers between **37** and **43**. _____

2) What are the next numbers?
   1, 5, 9, _____, _____

3) Which is an acute angle? _____

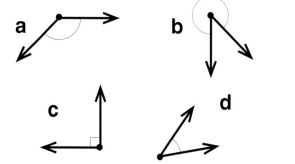

4) If **125** words fit on one page, how many pages would be needed to write a short story of **750** words? _____

5) What is the average (mean) of **15, 14** and **19**? _____

6) When you multiply a number by **6** and add **9** to the answer, you get **45**. What is the number? _____

7) Write $\frac{3}{10}$ as a decimal. _____

8) $7 - 4 - 2 = 7 - (5 - 1)$
   Is this true? _____

9) $80 \div 4 =$ _____ $\div \, 5$

10) Write **0.01** as a fraction. _____

11) Sweets are sold in bags of **10**. Andrew buys **14** bags for his friends. How many sweets do they have? _____

12) Paul can write **15** lines in **10** minutes. How many can he write in **2** hours? _____

13) How many sides does a hexagon have? _____

14) Which is a right angle? _____

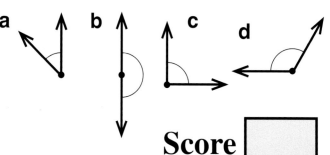

15) How many hours are there in a week? _____

Score [ ]   **Percentage** [ ] **%**

Do your workings on this page

Mark to %	
0	0%
1	7%
2	13%
3	20%
4	27%
5	33%
6	40%
7	47%
8	53%
9	60%
10	67%
11	73%
12	80%
13	87%
14	93%
15	100%

Maths Test 2

1) How any months do not have **31** days? _____

2) Deduct **seven hundredths** from **1.83**. _____

3) What is the sum of the following numbers that are divisible by **5**?

530   60   184   330 _____

4) What is the next number?

1, 13, 25, _____

5) The **3rd** triangular number is **6**. Write down the **4th** triangular number. _____

1st   ● (1)
2nd ●● (3)
3rd ●●● (6)

6) The walls in the room are

_____

(vertical, horizontal, diagonal)

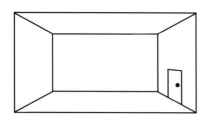

7) What is the highest number that is a factor of **48** and **60**? _____

8) Subtract the sum of **8** and **9** from the product of **8** and **9**.

_____

9) Which number in the group is not a factor of **36**? _____

(1, 2, 3, 4, 6, 8, 12, 18, 36)

10) What is the average of **4.5**, **6.0** and **1.5**?

_____

11) Which is the obtuse angle?_____

12) Which is the reflex angle?_____

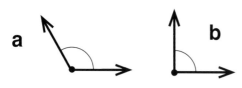

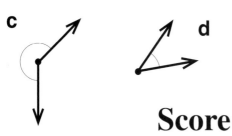

13) Change **486** hours to days and hours.

_____

14) Subtract $\frac{3}{4}$ from **2.5**.

_____

15) What is the next number?
96, **84**, **72,** _____

Score ☐   **Percentage** ☐ **%**

Do your workings on this page

Mark to %	
0	0%
1	7%
2	13%
3	20%
4	27%
5	33%
6	40%
7	47%
8	53%
9	60%
10	67%
11	73%
12	80%
13	87%
14	93%
15	100%

Maths Test 3

1) What is the next number? **1, 3, 9, 27,** _____

2) Reduce **3.25** by **1.75.**

_____

3) How many minutes is $11\frac{3}{4}$ hours?

_____

4) Rachel's grandfather died in **2006** at the age of **83**. In which year was he born? _____

5) The magic square adds up to **72** in each direction. What is the value of **A**?

_____

	18	28
	24	A
20		

6) What fraction of **1000** is **250**? _____

7) Write all the factors of **24.**

_____

8) What is the missing number?

56, 42, _____, **14**

9) How many seconds are there in one hour? _____

10) Take $\frac{1}{4}$ from **0.4.**

_____

11) What is the **fifth** triangular number? _____

1st	●	(1)
2nd	●●	(3)
3rd	●●●	(6)

12) $\frac{1}{2}$ of a number is **16**. What is $\frac{3}{4}$ of the same number? _____

13) What is the average of

5.5, **7.5** and **9.5**? _____

14) When you multiply a number by **nine** and add **sixteen** to your answer, you get **88**. What is the number?

_____

15) What day is the **14th** of April?

_____

MARCH						
Sun	Mon	Tue	Wed	Thu	Fri	Sat
		1	2	3	4	5
6	7	8	9	10	11	12

Score [ ] **Percentage** [ ] **%**

Do your workings on this page

Mark to %	
0	0%
1	7%
2	13%
3	20%
4	27%
5	33%
6	40%
7	47%
8	53%
9	60%
10	67%
11	73%
12	80%
13	87%
14	93%
15	100%

Maths Test 4

1) What is the next number?

   7, 9, 13, 21, ____

2) What is the sum of **three tenths** and **five hundredths**? _____

3) What date was the last day of **2007**? Write in figures. _____

4) $\dfrac{1}{12} = \dfrac{?}{60}$ _____

5) One container holds **12** crates. Each crate holds **8** bottles. How many bottles are there in **7** containers? _____

6) There are **one hundred** years in a century. How many centuries are there in a millennium? _____

7) What are the factors of **28**?

   _____

8) What number is halfway between **19** and **35**? _____

9) What are the common factors of **12** and **18**?

   _____

10) The **third** triangular number is **6**. What is the **sixth** triangular number? _____

11) Is this a reflex, acute or an obtuse angle? _____

12) What is the mean of

    19, 20, 26 and **31**? _____

13) Reduce **a hundred thousand** by **5**. Give your answer in figures. _____

14) Which is the obtuse angle? ____

15) Which is the acute angle? ____

a	b	c	d

 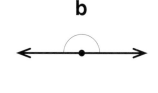  

Score   **Percentage** [ ] %

9

Do your workings on this page

Mark to %	
0	0%
1	7%
2	13%
3	20%
4	27%
5	33%
6	40%
7	47%
8	53%
9	60%
10	67%
11	73%
12	80%
13	87%
14	93%
15	100%

Maths Test 5

1) The value of each column and row only (not the diagonals) is the same.

What is the value **A**? _____

	A	14
	12	
10	12	6

---

2) **1984** was a leap year. Will **2028** be a leap year?

_____

3) What is the next fraction?

$\frac{1}{3}$, $\frac{1}{6}$, $\frac{1}{12}$, _____

---

4) Find the factors of **36**.

_____

5) What is the average of

13, **25**, **23**, **19**? _____

---

6) There are **90** degrees in a right angle. How many degrees are there in one complete turn of a circle? _____

---

7) What is the value of **B**? _____

8) What is the value of **C**? _____

26	16	B
	22	
C		18

9) $(105 \div 5) \times 5 =$ _____

10) Deduct **six tenths** from **1.55**.

_____

11) What is the sum of the odd numbers between **42** and **48**?

_____

---

12) Caroline is not as short as Melanie. Elaine is not as tall as Melanie. Who is the shortest?

_____

13) Start facing south. Turn clockwise to face east. How many right angles will you go through? _____

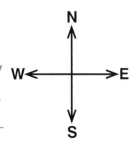

---

14) If **24** is subtracted from $\frac{1}{2}$ of a certain number the answer is **26**. What is the original number? _____

15) What fraction of this shape is shaded?

_____

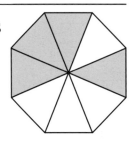

Score [ ]   **Percentage** [ ] **%**

Do your workings on this page

Mark to %	
0	0%
1	7%
2	13%
3	20%
4	27%
5	33%
6	40%
7	47%
8	53%
9	60%
10	67%
11	73%
12	80%
13	87%
14	93%
15	100%

Maths Test 6

1) What is the sum of the even numbers between **37** and **45**?

_____

2) What is the value of *t*?

$t - 13 = 2 \times 3$

_____

3) Harpreet is taller than Talvir but shorter than Mandip. Who is the tallest? _____

4) What is the value of **9** in **3.96**? _____

5) $7 - 13 =$ _____

6) How many days are there from the **24th** of June to the **11th** of July? _____

7) What is the **8th** triangular number? _____

8) One carton of mango juice holds **7** cups of juice. How many cups can be filled from **189** cartons?

_____

9) $3.7 + 7 + 0.03 =$ _____

10) What is the average of **13, 25, 23, 19**? _____

In what ratio are the:

11)

black and white marbles?
(B : W) _____

12) Die A   Die B

visible spots on the dice?
(A : B) _____

13) Domino X   Domino Y

 dots on these dominoes? (X : Y) _____

14) Timmy's watch is **4** minutes slow. At what time on his watch must he start his **12** minute journey to school if he has to be there at **8.45am**?

_____

15) Which of the letters below have perpendicular lines?

A F H M T Z

_____

Score [ ] Percentage [ ] %

Do your workings on this page

Mark to %	
0	0%
1	7%
2	13%
3	20%
4	27%
5	33%
6	40%
7	47%
8	53%
9	60%
10	67%
11	73%
12	80%
13	87%
14	93%
15	100%

Maths Test 7

1) Take **0.05** from **0.5** _____

2) $\dfrac{3}{5} = \dfrac{?}{40}$ _____

3) My uncle died in **2005** when he was **64**. When was he born? _____

4) Find the value of x in this equation:

$3x = 24 - 6$ _____

5) How many degrees are there in $1\frac{1}{3}$ right angles?

_____

6) If Cynthia was **three** times her present age, she would be **6** years younger than her mother who is **30**. How old is Cynthia? _____

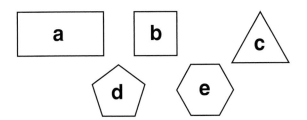

7) Which shape is a pentagon? _____

8) Which shape is not a regular polygon? _____

9) Draw a dot pattern to show that **10** is a triangular number.

10) What is value of n?

$20n = 100$ _____

11) Subtract **0.06** from **10.04** _____

12) $\dfrac{?}{8} = \dfrac{9}{24}$ _____

13) **£3.00** was shared among **6** girls and **8** boys. If each girl received **14p** and the rest was shared equally between the boys, how much did each boy receive? _____

14) **4** out of every **6** animals in a cage are rabbits. The rest are guinea pigs. What is the ratio of rabbits to guinea pigs? _____

15) How many days are there from the **23rd** of January to the **6th** of March in a leap year? (include both days) _____

Score ☐ Percentage ☐ %

Do your workings on this page

Mark to %	
0	0%
1	7%
2	13%
3	20%
4	27%
5	33%
6	40%
7	47%
8	53%
9	60%
10	67%
11	73%
12	80%
13	87%
14	93%
15	100%

Maths Test 8

1) Insert a decimal point so the **3** has a value of **three thousandths**.

89243 _____

2) Which of these numbers is both triangular and rectangular?

4, 18, 28, 47 _____

3) Which is an acute angle?

135°, 276°, 42°, 90°

_____

4) Put in order of size, largest first:

6.45, $6\frac{1}{2}$, 6.6

_____

5) What is the value of **9** in **673.192**?

_____

6) **34.16 × 10 =** _____

7) **11)3465 =** _____

8) A dart player hit **15** with her first dart, double **18** with her second and triple **12** with her third. What was her score? _____

9) There are **36** sweets in a packet. **27** are strawberry flavoured and the rest are apple flavoured. What is the simplest ratio of strawberry to apple flavoured sweets?

_____

10) A football match that lasts **90** minutes started at **1.30pm**. If the halftime break lasted **13** minutes and there were **three** minutes of injury time added on, at what time did the football match end? _____

11) **Five** out of every **9** children in a school bring in packed lunches. The rest of the children eat school lunches. What is the ratio of school lunches to packed lunches? _____

12) How many days are there altogether in October, November and December? _____

13) The news started at **10.15pm** and finished **1** hour **25** minutes later. At what time did it finish? _____

14) **41.7 × 100 =** _____

15) When some apples were shared, Nikita received $\frac{3}{5}$ of them. She gave **6** to Justin and had **15** left. How many apples were there altogether? _____

Score ☐ Percentage ☐ %

Do your workings on this page

Mark to %	
0	0%
1	7%
2	13%
3	20%
4	27%
5	33%
6	40%
7	47%
8	53%
9	60%
10	67%
11	73%
12	80%
13	87%
14	93%
15	100%

Maths Test 9

1) Sixteen is a square number.

Which of these are square numbers?

3, 18, 25, 27, 49 _____

2) What is the average of:

$$3\frac{1}{4}, \quad 1\frac{1}{2}, \quad 2\frac{3}{4}, \quad 4\frac{1}{2} \; ?$$

_____

3) $\frac{124}{2} = ?$ _____

4) A journalist is at her office from **8am** until **4.30pm**, **four** days a week. How many hours a week does she work? _____

5) $\frac{4}{8}$ is $\frac{1}{2}$ when simplified to its lowest terms. Write $\frac{14}{21}$ in its lowest terms. _____

6) What is the value of z?

$3z + 9 = 15$ _____

7) **137.75 ÷ 10 =** _____

8) What must be added to **63** so that it will divide exactly into **four** groups of **18**?

_____

9) Put in order of size, smallest first:

$\frac{52}{10}, \quad \frac{52}{100}, \quad$ **1.52**

_____

10) Which is a reflex angle?

325°, 47°, 90°, 75°

_____

11) Put in order of size, largest first:

4.02, $4\frac{1}{2}$ **, 4.1**

_____

12) 'If dominoes are placed at right angles to each other, they are _____ to each other.'

Complete the above sentence by inserting one of the following words: (parallel, perpendicular, horizontal, vertical, diagonal).

13) Lucy's watch is **seven** minutes slow. At what time on her watch must she start her journey to the station if she has to catch the **9.25am** train and if her walk to the station takes **12** minutes? _____

14) The product of **3** numbers is **126**. Two of the numbers are **6** and **3**. What is the **third** number? _____

15) $8\overline{)6472}$ = _____

Score ☐ Percentage ☐ %

Do your workings on this page

Mark to %	
0	0%
1	7%
2	13%
3	20%
4	27%
5	33%
6	40%
7	47%
8	53%
9	60%
10	67%
11	73%
12	80%
13	87%
14	93%
15	100%

Maths Test 10

1) Round **5.324** to **2** decimal places (**2 d.p.**).

_____

2) Find the missing number in this series:

98, 84, 71, 59, _____, 38

3) Which of these is a square number?
5, 11, 18, 24, 36, 47

_____

4) How many right angles are there in a full rotation?

_____

5) What is the highest common factor of **36** and **63**? _____

6) Find $\frac{5}{8}$ of **20**.

_____

7) **4.12 + 13.09 =** _____

8) **12** $\overline{)8064}$ **=** _____

9) A school conducted a survey of where children live. **160** children live in houses and **40** children live in flats. What is the ratio of children who live in houses to those who live in flats? Give your answer in its simplest form. _____

10) Deduct **four thousand** from **400,000** _____

11) How many **hundredths** are there in **1.63**? _____

12) What is the mean of:
24, 16, 26, 20? _____

13) What is the missing number?
3, 6, 12, _____, 48, 96

14) Ryan does his homework for **three quarters** of an hour each day, for **six** days a week. What is the total time he spends on homework in one week? _____

15) If Kevin was **four** times his present age, he would be **five** years older than his mother, who is **27**. How old is Kevin now? _____

Score [ ]   **Percentage** [ ] **%**

Do your workings on this page

Mark to %	
0	0%
1	7%
2	13%
3	20%
4	27%
5	33%
6	40%
7	47%
8	53%
9	60%
10	67%
11	73%
12	80%
13	87%
14	93%
15	100%

Maths Test 11

1) $3.48 \div 1.2 =$ _____

2) $2.030 \times 100 =$ _____

3) Polly is at school from **8.30am** until **4.30pm**. What fraction of the day does she spend at school? _____

4) Add the odd numbers between **32** and **42**. _____

5) What are the factors of **17**?

_____

6) What fraction of a full rotation is **60°**?
$\frac{1}{5}$, $\frac{1}{6}$, $\frac{1}{3}$ _____

7) What is the next number?

8, **11**, **16**, **23**, _____

8) **Four** out of every **seven** children in a class are girls. If there are **16** girls, how many children are there altogether? _____

9) The two triangular numbers **10** and **6** make the square number **16**.

What two triangular numbers make this square number?

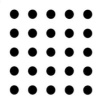 _____

10) How many triangles are there here? _____

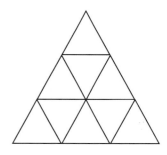

11) What is the value of x?
$8x - 11 = 61$ _____

12) Tayyib was **23** in **2007**. How old was he in **1988**? _____

13) What must you multiply **14** by to get half of **112**? _____

14) What is the value of the **4** in **12.346**? _____

15) **23** is a prime number. A prime number has no other factors except itself and _____ .

Score [ ] **Percentage** [ ] **%**

Do your workings on this page

Mark to %	
0	0%
1	7%
2	13%
3	20%
4	27%
5	33%
6	40%
7	47%
8	53%
9	60%
10	67%
11	73%
12	80%
13	87%
14	93%
15	100%

Maths Test 12

1) $43 - 9 = \frac{1}{3}$ of _____

2) $0.13 \times 3.8 =$ _____

3) What is the next prime number?

   53, 59, 61, _____

4) Round **1.67** to **1 d.p.**

   _____

5) A clock shows a time of **4.15pm**. Through how many degrees must the minute hand turn to show a time of **5.00pm**? _____

6) Which number in this list is a prime number? _____

   9, 13, 28, 39, 51

7) $\frac{5}{12}$ of **204** = _____

8) My book has **72** pages. I have read $\frac{5}{9}$ of them. How many pages do I still have to read? _____

9) Add the odd numbers between **92** and **102**. _____

10) Is **15** a rectangular number?

    _____

11) The ratio of men to women in a tennis club is **3:2**. If there are **60** men, how many women are there? _____

12) 4^2 is greater than 2^4.
    Is this statement true or false? _____

13) Red and yellow sweets in a jar are in the ratio of **4:1**.
    If there are **80** sweets altogether, how many red sweets are there?

    _____

14) If you add one odd number to one even number, is the answer odd or even? _____

15) Add the prime numbers between **8** and **20**. _____

Score [ ] **Percentage** [ ] **%**

Do your workings on this page

Mark to %	
0	0%
1	7%
2	13%
3	20%
4	27%
5	33%
6	40%
7	47%
8	53%
9	60%
10	67%
11	73%
12	80%
13	87%
14	93%
15	100%

Maths Test 13

1) Which number is **10** times smaller than **a hundred thousand**?

   _____

2) $\frac{2}{9} \times \frac{3}{16} =$ ____

3) $9 + 6 + 3 +$ ____ $= 6^2$

4) Which is the largest?

   $\frac{1}{4}$ $\frac{1}{3}$ $\frac{3}{16}$ $\frac{5}{12}$ ____

5) What is the next number?

   0, 3, 9, 21, ____

6) Anne-Marie's watch is **7** minutes slow. At what time on her watch must she start her **20** minute journey to the train station to catch the **8.52am** train? _____

7) Which shape is not symmetrical? ____

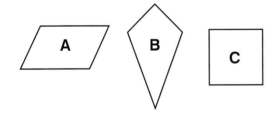

8) How many axes of symmetry does this rhombus have? _____

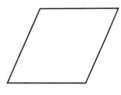

9) What number is 3^3? _____

10) $18 \overline{)8064} =$ _____

11) **Four** out of **seven** boys in a class have a computer at home. If **12** boys do not have a computer, how many do have them? _____

12) Convert the mixed number $5\frac{7}{9}$ into an improper fraction. _____

13) My uncle was born in **1963**. In what year will he be **65** years old?

   _____

14) Give the value of the **3** in **821.37**. _____

15) $8^2 + 11^3 + 12^3 =$ _____

Score [ ]   **Percentage** [ ] **%**

Do your workings on this page

Mark to %	
0	0%
1	7%
2	13%
3	20%
4	27%
5	33%
6	40%
7	47%
8	53%
9	60%
10	67%
11	73%
12	80%
13	87%
14	93%
15	100%

Maths Test 14

1) $16\overline{)1345}$ = _____ Give your answer to **1 d.p.**

2) $2\frac{1}{3} \times 1\frac{1}{14} =$ _____

3) **Three** out of every **seven** boys in a class like playing football. If **21** boys enjoy playing football, how many do not? _____

4) What is the next number?

   0.3, **0.4**, **0.6**, **0.9**, _____

5) How many degrees are there in $\frac{4}{5}$ of a full rotation? _____

6) $\frac{2}{7}$ of **168** = _____

7) **2.1 ÷ 0.3 =** _____

8) $6^3 \div 3^2 =$ _____

9)

MARCH						
Sun	Mon	Tue	Wed	Thu	Fri	Sat
		1	**2**	**3**	**4**	**5**
6	**7**	**8**	**9**	**10**	**11**	**12**

What day was the **13th** of February?
(It is <u>not</u> a leap year).

_____

10) Use +, −, × or ÷ to complete the following:

   40 ÷ 8 = 15 ___ 10

11) What is the missing number?

   5, 8, 13, 20, _____, 40

12) What is the next fraction?

   1, $\frac{1}{2}$, $\frac{1}{4}$, ___

13) Does this shape have rotational symmetry? (yes or no)

   _____

14) Sam gave **one sixth** of his marbles to Peter but still has **20** left. How many did he give to Peter? _____

15) A doctor working on day shift starts at **8.45am** and finishes at **6.15pm**. How many hours does he work if he works for **5** consecutive days?

   _____ hours and _____ minutes.

Score [ ]   Percentage [ ] %

Do your workings on this page

Mark to %	
0	0%
1	7%
2	13%
3	20%
4	27%
5	33%
6	40%
7	47%
8	53%
9	60%
10	67%
11	73%
12	80%
13	87%
14	93%
15	100%

Maths Test 15

1) $0.5 \times £19 =$ _____

2) $9^2 = 33 +$ _____

3) Hayley is facing west. If she turns left (anti-clockwise) through two right angles, in what direction will she be facing? _____

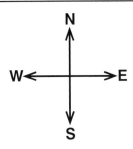

4) $(11 \times 6) + (11 \times 4) = 11 \times$ _____

5) $\frac{10}{21} \div \frac{5}{14} =$ _____

6) $15\overline{\smash{)}7186} =$ _____ Write your answer as a decimal to **2 d.p.**

7) Trains leave Paddington Station every **10** minutes from **7.30am**. At what time will the **fifth** train leave? _____

8) What is the total of the odd numbers between **96** and **104**?

_____

9) What fraction of a full rotation is **300°**?

_____

10) What two triangular numbers make this square number?

_____ and _____

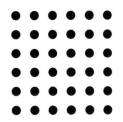

11) Find the average of:

0.3, 3, 30

_____

12) **84** mints are shared among **12** boys and **18** girls. If each girl received **2** mints, how many did each boy receive? _____

13) Fill in the missing number of the sequence.

32, 30, 26, _____, 12

14) What fraction of **9** is $1\frac{1}{2}$?

_____

15) What is $\frac{5}{12}$ as a decimal to **2 d.p.**? _____

Score [ ] **Percentage** [ ] **%**

Do your workings on this page

Mark to %	
0	0%
1	7%
2	13%
3	20%
4	27%
5	33%
6	40%
7	47%
8	53%
9	60%
10	67%
11	73%
12	80%
13	87%
14	93%
15	100%

Maths Test 16

1) What is the next fraction?

$$1, \ \frac{1}{5}, \ \frac{1}{25}, \ \frac{1}{125}, \ \_\_\_\_$$

2) $6n + 3 = 45$

What is the value of n?

_____

3) How many passengers can be seated on a bus which seats **four** passengers in each of its **15** rows? _____

4) What are the **second** and **third** rectangular numbers?

_____

5) $0.06 \times 130 =$ _____

6) $12^2 - 11^2 =$ _____

7) $7.5\text{km} + 750\text{m} - 0.45\text{km} =$ _____ km

8) $1\frac{3}{5} \div 1\frac{1}{15} =$ _____

9) $25 \div (4^2 - 11) =$ _____

10) Dave is facing northeast. If he turned anti-clockwise through an angle of **270°**, in what direction would he be facing? _____

11) The middle number of five consecutive odd numbers is **103**. What is the **first** number? _____

12) The year **1819** was in which century?

_____

13) **9** litres of juice cost **£12.60**. How much does **5** litres cost? _____

14) The ratio of boys to girls on a funfair ride is **4:5**. There are **45** children altogether. How many are girls? _____

15) Brendan was **4** years and **5** months old in January **2004**. In which year and what month was he born?

_____

Score [ ]   Percentage [ ] %

Do your workings on this page

Mark to %	
0	0%
1	7%
2	13%
3	20%
4	27%
5	33%
6	40%
7	47%
8	53%
9	60%
10	67%
11	73%
12	80%
13	87%
14	93%
15	100%

Maths Test 17

1) Write **2%** as a decimal _____

2) **0.9** of **18** = _____

3) What is the mean of **31**, **35** and **33**? _____

4) $1\frac{1}{2} + \frac{13}{16} =$ _____

5) A football game that lasts **90** minutes started at **3.45pm**. The half-time break lasted **12** minutes and there were **6** minutes added on at the end for stoppages. At what time did the game finish? _____

6) Mr and Mrs Smith take their **3** boys to the cinema. Adult tickets cost **£8.50** and child tickets cost **£4.25**. Popcorn costs **£1.75** for each child. How much change does Mr Smith receive from a **£50** note?

_____

7) **197 × 15** = _____

8) **13** $\overline{)1489}$ = _____
Give your answer to the nearest whole number.

9) Write **56%** as a fraction in its lowest terms. _____

10) What are the values of **A**, **B** and **C**?

A	12	20
C	18	
16		B

A = _____

B = _____

C = _____

11) What is the sum of the first **eight** even numbers?

_____

12) What is the next fraction?

$\frac{4}{1}$, $\frac{8}{2}$, $\frac{12}{3}$, _____

13) If I share **80** oranges between **2** people in the ratio **9:11**, how many oranges will they each receive? _____

14) A cinema has **14** rows of **26** seats on one side and **12** rows of **23** seats on the other side. How many seats are there altogether? _____

15) The _____ is the length around the outside of a circle. (circumference, diameter, radius)

Score [   ]   Percentage [   ] %

Do your workings on this page

Mark to %	
0	0%
1	7%
2	13%
3	20%
4	27%
5	33%
6	40%
7	47%
8	53%
9	60%
10	67%
11	73%
12	80%
13	87%
14	93%
15	100%

Maths Test 18

1) What is the highest factor of **39** (other than **39**)? _____

2) $2\frac{1}{9} - 1\frac{5}{6} =$ _____

3) What is **0.625** as a fraction? _____

4) Anne is facing southwest. If she turns anti-clockwise through an angle of **180°**, in what direction will she be facing? _____

5) Stuart sleeps from **9pm** until **6am**. What fraction of a day does he spend asleep? _____

6) If $a = 14$ and $b = 7$, then

$a^2 \div b^2 =$ _____

7) $10^4 =$ _____

8) $14\overline{)7891} =$ _____

Write your answer as a decimal to **2 d.p.**

9) Write $\frac{13}{20}$ as a percentage. _____

10) The radius of a circle is half the length of the _____.
(circumference, perimeter, tangent, diameter)

11) **2** is a factor of **8**.
2 is also a factor of **12**.
2 is a common factor of **8** and **12**.
Name two common factors of **27** and **36** (excluding **1**). _____

12) There is only one prime number which is also an even number.

It is _____

13) A multiple of **4** is any number that has **4** as a factor. Which is not a multiple of **4**?

80, 12, 36, 48, 82, 88

_____

14) What fraction of this shape is shaded? _____

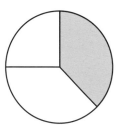

15) A watch is **11** minutes slow and shows **9.25am**. Another watch is **11** minutes fast. What is the time on the second watch? _____

Score _____   Percentage _____ %

Do your workings on this page

Mark to %	
0	0%
1	7%
2	13%
3	20%
4	27%
5	33%
6	40%
7	47%
8	53%
9	60%
10	67%
11	73%
12	80%
13	87%
14	93%
15	100%

Maths Test 19

1) $4^3 + 13^2 =$ _____

2) Write $\frac{9}{20}$ as a percentage. _____

3) $3^2 - 2^3 =$ _____

4) What is **15%** of **200**? _____

5) Fill in the missing numbers:

49, 64, ___ , 100, 121, ___ , 169

6) $16\overline{\smash{)}3128} =$ _____

(Write your answer as a decimal).

7) Put in size order, smallest first:

4.03, 4.3, 4.043

_____

8) Find the highest common factor (HCF) of **48** and **36**.

_____

9) Insert a decimal point so that the **4** has a value of **four thousandths**.

5 3 1 7 4   _____

10) Which of these regular polygons is an octagon? _____

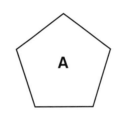
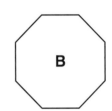
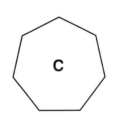
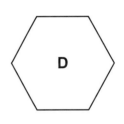

A   B   C   D

11) This is a clock face in a mirror. What is the time in figures?

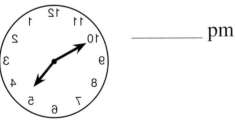 _____ pm

12) Which of these are multiples of **9**?

12, 26, 47, 54, 55, 108

_____

13) Write $\frac{9}{1000}$ as a decimal.

_____

14) $(36 \times 7) + (36 \times 3) =$ _____

15)

Y		20
Z		
18	22	17

What are the values of **Y** and **Z**?

Y = _____

Z = _____

Score [   ]   Percentage [   ] %

Do your workings on this page

Mark to %	
0	0%
1	7%
2	13%
3	20%
4	27%
5	33%
6	40%
7	47%
8	53%
9	60%
10	67%
11	73%
12	80%
13	87%
14	93%
15	100%

Maths Test 20

1) $10^3 - 9^2 =$ _____

2) Change from a % to a fraction:

   $72\% =$ _____

3) Put in size order, smallest first:

   3.3, 3.299, 3.33

   _____

4) What is the value of *y*?

   $\frac{y}{7} = 6$

   $y =$ ____

5) **30%** of people drive to work, **22%** cycle, **7%** walk and the rest travel by bus. What percentage travel by bus? _____

6) Which of these triangles is a regular polygon?

   _____

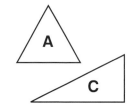 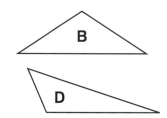

7) What is **90%** of **330**? _____

8) Increase **125g** by **44%**. _____

9) Fill in the missing number:

   289, 256, 225, ____, 169

10) $15\overline{)1938} =$ _____

   (Write your answer as a decimal).

11) **Sixteen** is a multiple of **2**. It is also a multiple of **8**. Which of these numbers are multiples of both **4** and **8**?

   22, 32, 36, 40, 42

   _____

12) A greengrocer sells **51** apples on Saturday and an average of **30** apples on each of the other **six** days. What is her daily average for the whole week? _____

13) If you add an odd number to an odd number, will the answer be odd or even? _____

14) Is this true?

   0.2 < 0.199

   _____

15) $13^2 + 14^2 =$ _____

Score [ ]   Percentage [ ] %

Do your workings on this page

Mark	to %
0	0%
1	7%
2	13%
3	20%
4	27%
5	33%
6	40%
7	47%
8	53%
9	60%
10	67%
11	73%
12	80%
13	87%
14	93%
15	100%

Maths Test 21

1) $(8 \times 9) - (6 \times 9) =$ _____

2) $16^2 + 6^2 - 3^2 =$ _____

3) What is the sum of the first **4** prime numbers? (**1** is not counted as a prime number). _____

4) What is the next number?

   1000, 100, 10, _____

5) What is **150m** as a % of **7.5km**?

   _____

6) If $x = 5$ and $y = 2$, then

   $2x + 3y =$ _____

7) Which of these are common multiples of **8** and **16**?

   12, 16, 20, 24, 28, 32, 40, 48

   _____

8) Which shape is a regular polygon?
   - rhombus
   - square
   - isosceles triangle
   - rectangle

   _____

9) What is the next number?

   8, 27, 64, _____

   (Clue: what is 2^3?)

10) What is the next number?

    10, 5, $2\frac{1}{2}$, _____

11) Stephen exchanged $\frac{3}{5}$ of his **45** stickers for **11** of Peter's. How many stickers does Stephen have now? _____

12) In a class of **30, 70%** passed a test. How many children did not pass the test? _____

13) Put in size order, largest first:

    $\frac{1}{12}$, **0.08, 9%**

    _____

14) What is the sum of the odd numbers between **50** and **56**? _____

15)

JUNE						
Sun	Mon	Tue	Wed	Thu	Fri	Sat
		1	2	3	4	5
6	7	8	9	10	11	12

On what day is the **27th** of July?

_____

Score ☐   **Percentage** ☐ **%**

43

Do your workings on this page

Mark to %	
0	0%
1	7%
2	13%
3	20%
4	27%
5	33%
6	40%
7	47%
8	53%
9	60%
10	67%
11	73%
12	80%
13	87%
14	93%
15	100%

Maths Test 22

1) Complete the following equation:

$$84 = 3 \times 4 \times \underline{\hspace{1cm}}$$

2) $\dfrac{1.6}{0.8} = \underline{\hspace{0.7cm}}$

3) What is **6%** of **450**? _____

4) $7 \times 7 \times 7 = 7^3$ (7 cubed) = **343**

What is 8^3? _____

5) $16^2 - 7^2 = \underline{\hspace{1cm}}$

6) What is **12%** of **£25**? _____

7) $(7 \times 6) + (5 \times 2^3) = \underline{\hspace{1cm}}$

8) What is the size of angle **A** in the following right-angled triangle?

_____

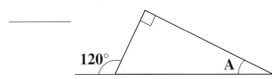

9) If the date is Sunday the **25th** of September, what day will the **31st** of October be?

_____

10) A box contains pencils and rubbers in the ratio **3:7**. If there are **24** pencils, how many rubbers are there? _____

11) What is the size of angle **A** in the quadrilateral below? _____

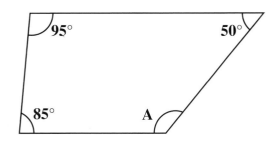

12) What is the next number in the sequence?

0.04, 0.4, 4, 40, _____

13) Which of these numbers is rectangular?

11, 13, 15, 17, 19 _____

14) What are the values of **A**, **B** and **C**?

19	C	B
	11	18
A		3

A = _____

B = _____

C = _____

15) Andrea has **£65** and Robert has **£91**. Express these amounts as a ratio.

_____ : _____

Score   Percentage [   ] %

Do your workings on this page

Mark to %	
0	0%
1	7%
2	13%
3	20%
4	27%
5	33%
6	40%
7	47%
8	53%
9	60%
10	67%
11	73%
12	80%
13	87%
14	93%
15	100%

Maths Test 23

1) $9^3 - 7^3 =$ _____

2) $98 \times 10,000 =$ _____

3) A factor that is also a prime number is called a prime factor.
The prime factors of **24** can be written as $2 \times 2 \times 2 \times 3$ or $2^3 \times 3$.
The prime factors of **20** can be written as $2^2 \times$ _____

4) What is the next number in the series?

500, 50, 5, _____

5) $\dfrac{1.8}{0.09} =$ _____

6) What are the values of **A** and **B**?

A		13
11	12	13
	15	B

A = _____

B = _____

7) $6 \times 666 =$ _____

8) $3^2 + 5^2 + 2^3 =$ _____

9) _____ $- 4^2 = 3^2$

10) Geoff did **three** maths tests. He got **75%** in the first paper, **41%** in the next and **64%** in the third. What was his mean percentage?

_____

11) The temperature was -2°C during the night. The next day it rose to **8°C**. How many degrees warmer was it then? _____

12) What is **30%** of **300**? _____

13) $\dfrac{16}{40} =$ _____ %

14) **A quarter** of the pupils in a P.E. class do not play rounders. **24** children play. How many do not play? _____

15) What is the size of angle **A**?

_____

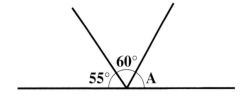

Score [ ] Percentage [ ] %

Do your workings on this page

Mark to %	
0	0%
1	7%
2	13%
3	20%
4	27%
5	33%
6	40%
7	47%
8	53%
9	60%
10	67%
11	73%
12	80%
13	87%
14	93%
15	100%

Maths Test 24

1) Convert this decimal to a %.

  1.12 = _____

2) What is **45p** as a % of **£5**?

  _____

3) Which of these is a multiple of **4**?

  13, 27, 44, 46

  _____

4) The prime factors of **48** are **2⁴** and _____

5) $15^3 + 6^3 =$ _____

6) What fraction of **one** hour is **45** minutes? _____

  (Give the answer in lowest terms).

7) What is the size of angle **B**?

  _____

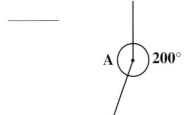

8) How many **thousands** are in $\frac{1}{4}$ of a **million**? _____

9) What is the size of angle **A**?

  _____

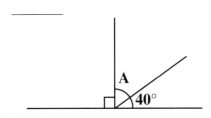

10) What is the size of angle **A**?

  _____

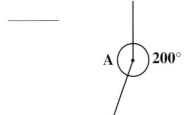

11) Which of these are common multiples of **6** and **9**?

  9, 12, 18, 27, 30, 36

  _____

12) What is the size of angle **C**?

  _____

13) Put in size order, largest first:

  $\frac{7}{20}$, **0.36**, **34.5%**

  _____

14) **5** out of every **7** children in a class like maths. If **8** dislike maths, how many children are there in the class? _____

15) Which fraction is greater than $\frac{1}{2}$ but less than $\frac{3}{4}$?

  $\frac{2}{5}$, $\frac{5}{6}$, $\frac{5}{8}$, $\frac{9}{10}$ _____

Score [ ] **Percentage** [%]

Do your workings on this page

Mark to %	
0	0%
1	7%
2	13%
3	20%
4	27%
5	33%
6	40%
7	47%
8	53%
9	60%
10	67%
11	73%
12	80%
13	87%
14	93%
15	100%

Maths Test 25

1) $(2 + 6)^2 - (3^2 + 4^2) \times 2 =$ _____

2) If **5** children can build a tree house in **12** days, how long will it take **4** children to complete the same task? _____

3) Which of these are common multiples of **4** and **7**?

4, 21, 24, 28, 49, 56

_____

4) $17 \overline{)3964} =$ _____

Write your answer correct to **2 d.p.**

5) $3^4 \times 4 =$ _____

6) What is the next number?

60, 6, 0.6, _____

7) What is the lowest common multiple of **5, 6** and **8**? _____

8) One winter's day the temperature was **5°C**. That night it dropped to **-7°C**. How many degrees colder was it that night? _____

9) Two angles of a triangle are of size **60°** and **20°**. What is the size of the third angle? _____

10) When $\frac{2}{5}$ of a certain number is reduced by **17** the result is **23**. What is the original number? _____

11) **15%** of **300** runners in a marathon gave up before the end of the race. How many finished the race? _____

12) The prime factors of **45** are 3^2 and _____

13) If a 'fair' pack of **52** playing cards is shuffled, what is the probability of drawing a Jack, a Queen or a King? _____

14) What would Navraj score on a dart board if he hit triple **12** with his first dart, **17** with his second and double **15** with his third? _____

15) Pete is not as tall as Ranjeev. Ranjeev is not as short as Ravi. Who is the tallest? _____

Score [　] **Percentage** [　] **%**

Do your workings on this page

Mark to %	
0	0%
1	7%
2	13%
3	20%
4	27%
5	33%
6	40%
7	47%
8	53%
9	60%
10	67%
11	73%
12	80%
13	87%
14	93%
15	100%

Maths Test 26

1) Take **two hundred thousand** from **two million**. _____

2) How many degrees does the minute hand of a clock turn through from a time of **4.47pm** to **5.11pm**? _____

3) The middle number of **7** consecutive odd numbers is **37**. What is the **second** number in this series? _____

4) $1 \div$ _____ $= 0.001$

5) $18 \overline{)3004} =$ _____ Give your answer to **2 d.p.**

6) What is the highest common factor of **36**, **18** and **54**? _____

7) The prime factors of a number are 2^5 and **3**. What is the number? _____

8) What is the lowest common multiple (LCM) of **6**, **8** and **12**? _____

9) Increase **£3.60** by **15%**. _____

10) In a large bag of sweets there are **14** green sweets, **twice** as many yellow sweets and **seven** times as many red sweets. How many sweets are there in the bag? _____

11) Which of these letters have parallel lines?

   A   D   F   G   M   Z

   _____

12) $x = 4$ and $y = 7$

   $x^3 + 4y =$ _____

13) The temperature on a cold night is **-5**°C. What will the temperature be in the morning if it rises by **8**°C? _____

14) There are **15** rows of **18** seats on each side of an amateur football ground. What is the total number of seats on all **four** sides of the ground? _____

15) 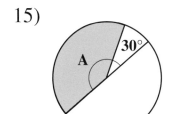 Write the shaded sector **A** as a fraction of a full rotation. **A =** _____

Score [ ]   **Percentage** [ ] **%**

Do your workings on this page

Mark to %	
0	0%
1	7%
2	13%
3	20%
4	27%
5	33%
6	40%
7	47%
8	53%
9	60%
10	67%
11	73%
12	80%
13	87%
14	93%
15	100%

Maths Test 27

1) $2.24 \times 1.6 =$ _____

2) What is **65%** of **350**? _____

3) What is the lowest common multiple (LCM) of **8** and **9**? _____

4) $16\overline{)9847} =$ _____

Give your answer to **1 d.p.**

5) A shopkeeper mixed **140** red flowers with **80** yellow flowers to make bunches of **11**. How many bunches can he make? _____

6) How many minutes is $\frac{7}{12}$ of an hour? _____

7) What is the **25th** odd number? _____

8) What is the fewest number of chocolate bars that can be arranged in multipacks of either **4, 6** or **9**? _____

9) What is the value of **A** in this magic square? _____

Total in all directions = **48**

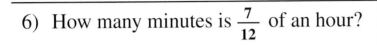

19		15
A	16	
	18	

10) What is the highest factor of **40**? _____

11) $(0 \times 4) \div 4 =$ _____

12) What is the missing number?

15, 18, 24, ____ , 45, 60

13) A pet shop has a number of kittens. The ratio of female to male kittens is **3:2**. There are **15** kittens altogether. How many female kittens are there? _____

14) What is the size of angle **A**? _____

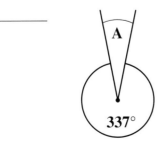

337°

15) On a plan, a school field is drawn to a scale of **3cm** to **8m**. If the width of the field is **20m**, what would this measure on the plan? _____ cm

Score [ ]   **Percentage** [ ] **%**

Do your workings on this page

Mark to %	
0	0%
1	7%
2	13%
3	20%
4	27%
5	33%
6	40%
7	47%
8	53%
9	60%
10	67%
11	73%
12	80%
13	87%
14	93%
15	100%

Maths Test 28

1) What is this shape?

_____

2) What is **51p** out of **85p** as a percentage? _____

3) $16^2 =$ _____

4) What number, when divided by **100**, gives **100**? _____

5) $100 - 34 = 6 \times$ ____

6) **40%** of **75** = _____

7) What is the size of angle **A**?

_____

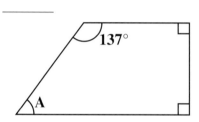

8) What is the missing number?

3.0, **3.4**, ____, **3.9**, **4.0**

9) What is the largest remainder you can have when you divide by **29**? _____

10) Victoria is $1\frac{1}{2}$ times older than her brother Nick. If Victoria is **15**, how old is Nick? _____

11) Which is the odd one out? _____

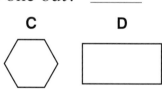

12) The temperature is **-9°C**. What will it be if it rises by **16°C**?

_____

13) The middle number of **7** consecutive even numbers is **388**. What is the first number in this series? _____

14) There are **3** minutes of advertising for every **15** minutes of television time. If this pattern was repeated for every hour of TV, what fraction of an hour would be used for advertising? _____

15)

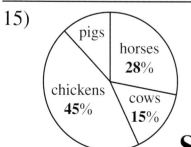

What fraction of the farm animals are pigs? _____

Score ☐ Percentage ☐ %

Do your workings on this page

Mark to %	
0	0%
1	7%
2	13%
3	20%
4	27%
5	33%
6	40%
7	47%
8	53%
9	60%
10	67%
11	73%
12	80%
13	87%
14	93%
15	100%

Maths Test 29

1) What is the size of angle **B**?

_____

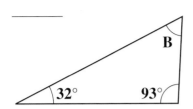

2) **19²** = _____

3) What is $\frac{1}{3}$ of $\frac{1}{15}$? _____

4) Reduce **800** by **15%** _____

5) What is this shape?

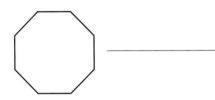 _____

6) What is the size of angle **B**?

_____

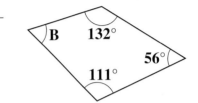

7) What is the highest common factor of **96**, **132** and **144**?

_____

8) Solve this equation:

$2a + b + 3c =$ _____

$a = 4 \quad b = 6 \quad c = 3$

9) A coach holds **37** passengers. If there are **450** passengers to be transported, how many coaches will be needed? _____

10) What is **1.6kg** out of **4kg** as a %?

_____

11) $27\overline{)4569}$ = _____

(Give your answer as a decimal to **2 d.p.**)

12) What is the size of angle **Z**?

_____

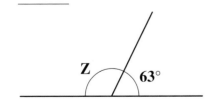

13) **13³** = _____

14) Fill in the missing number.

$$19\overline{)}\ \ ^{6\ r\ 11}$$

15) Rachel scored **52** marks out of **65** in a test. What percentage did she achieve? _____

Score ☐ **Percentage** ☐ **%**

Do your workings on this page

Mark to %	
0	0%
1	7%
2	13%
3	20%
4	27%
5	33%
6	40%
7	47%
8	53%
9	60%
10	67%
11	73%
12	80%
13	87%
14	93%
15	100%

Maths Test 30

1) Sweets are shared out between Claire and Jessica in the ratio **2:5**. If Claire received **10** sweets, how many did Jessica receive? _____

2) What is the next number in this sequence?

3, 5, 4, 10, 5, 15, _____

3) What is the LCM of **3, 4** and **5**?

_____

4) A clock loses **5** seconds every hour. How many minutes will it lose in **2** days? _____

5) $a = 4 \quad b = 5 \quad c = 6$

Solve the equation:

$3c + b - 2a =$ _____

6) Which whole numbers are greater than **-7** but less than **-3**?

_____

7) What is the highest common factor of **66, 132** and **154**?

_____

8) Kyle has **116** conkers. He keeps **52** for himself and shares the rest equally between his **four** friends. How many conkers does each friend get? _____

9) **96** children in a school go home for lunch. **20%** do not. How many children are there in the school? _____

10) Which of these is an isosceles triangle?

_____

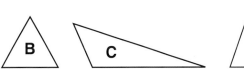

11) Which **2** consecutive square numbers have a difference of **9**? _____

12) $20 \overline{)3242} =$ _____

Give your answer as a decimal.

13) What is $\frac{1}{4}$ of $\frac{3}{8}$? _____

14) Gurdeep and Jagdeep's mum shares out some money between them in the ratio **9:7**. If Jagdeep was given **£5.60**, how much did Gurdeep receive? _____

15) What is the size of angle **A**?

_____

Score [ ] Percentage [ ] %

Do your workings on this page

Mark to %	
0	0%
1	7%
2	13%
3	20%
4	27%
5	33%
6	40%
7	47%
8	53%
9	60%
10	67%
11	73%
12	80%
13	87%
14	93%
15	100%

Maths Test 31

1) $3.85 \div 1.1 =$ _____

2) $\frac{1}{3} + \frac{1}{9} + \frac{11}{36} =$ _____

3) What is the lowest common multiple (LCM) of **3**, **7** and **9**? _____

4) $23\overline{)6491} =$ _____

Give the answer as a decimal (**2 d.p.**).

5) What are the values of **A** and **B**?

B		25
	24	
23	A	20

A = _____

B = _____

6) What is the size of angle **B**? _____

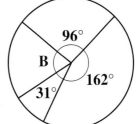

7) Put in size order, starting with the smallest.

13%, $\frac{31}{100}$, $\frac{1}{13}$ _____

8) Find the highest common factor (HCF) of **64**, **96** and **112**. _____

9) The prime factors of a number are **7** and 2^3. What is the number? _____

10) $17^3 + 13^3 =$ _____

11) What is the **7th** rectangular number? _____

12) Write in size order, starting with the smallest.

2, -1, 5, -12, 0, -2, 1

_____

13) What is the size of angle **A**? _____

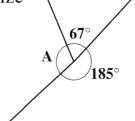

14) This is a clock in a mirror. What is the time?

_____ am

15) What fraction of this circle is shaded? _____

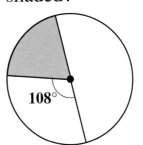

Score **Percentage** _____ **%**

Do your workings on this page

© 2008 Stephen Curran

Mark to %	
0	0%
1	7%
2	13%
3	20%
4	27%
5	33%
6	40%
7	47%
8	53%
9	60%
10	67%
11	73%
12	80%
13	87%
14	93%
15	100%

Maths Test 32

1) How many faces does a cuboid have? _____

2) What is the **18th** odd number? _____

3) What is the missing number?

   1825, 182.5, _____, 1.825

4) Is a pyramid a prism?

   (yes or no) _____

5) **184** children in a school are right-handed. **8%** are not. How many children are left-handed? _____

6) The average age of three girls is **10** years. One girl is **11** years old and the second is **12** years old. How old is the third girl? _____

7) How many angles does a dodecagon have? _____

8) $\frac{1}{25} \times 5 =$ _____

9) **3 ÷ 0.5 =** _____

10) What fraction of the circle is shaded?

$\frac{1}{12}, \frac{1}{10}, \frac{1}{8}, \frac{1}{4}$

_____

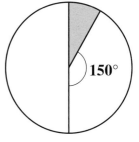

11) Write the next number in the sequence.

   10.24, 2.56, 0.64, 0.16, _____

12) What is the LCM of **12, 14** and **21**? _____

13) **2pm** on a 24-hour clock is **14:00**. What is **7.20pm**? _____

14) $16 \overline{)8948}$ = _____ Give your answer to **1 d.p.**

15) What is the size of angle **A** in this triangle?

_____

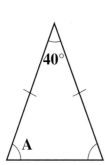

Score [ ] **Percentage** [ ] **%**

Do your workings on this page

Mark to %	
0	0%
1	7%
2	13%
3	20%
4	27%
5	33%
6	40%
7	47%
8	53%
9	60%
10	67%
11	73%
12	80%
13	87%
14	93%
15	100%

Maths Test 33

1) What is the smallest number that can be divided by **400**, **600** or **900**? _____

2) What is the missing number?

   9072, 1512, 252, _____ , 7

3) What is the HCF of **39**, **52** and **78**? _____

4) 7^2 is a prime factor of **539**. What is the other prime factor? _____

5) What number is halfway between **-5** and **+7**? _____

6) Mr Davis takes the overnight train from Cornwall to London. He arrives in London at **07:14**. If the journey takes **6** hrs **35** mins, at what time did he depart? _____

7) What fraction of an hour is **36** minutes? Write the fraction in its lowest terms. _____

8) $1.5^2 = $ _____

9) The average age of **three** people is **26**. If one is **24** and another is **28**, how old is the **third** person? _____

10) Holly scored **96** out of **150** in a maths test. What percentage did she achieve? _____

11) A multiple of **4** is any number that has **4** as a factor. Which is not a multiple of **4**?

    20, 52, 76, 106, 124 _____

12) The average age of **four** men is **28**. The age of **three** of them is **25**. What is the age of the **fourth** man? _____

13) $22 \overline{)2599}$ = _____ Give your answer to **2 d.p.**

14) Write **22:08** using **am** or **pm**. _____

15) What is the size of angle **A**? _____

135° 106°

Score ☐ Percentage ☐ %

Do your workings on this page

Mark to %	
0	0%
1	7%
2	13%
3	20%
4	27%
5	33%
6	40%
7	47%
8	53%
9	60%
10	67%
11	73%
12	80%
13	87%
14	93%
15	100%

Maths Test 34

1) $(13^2 + 2^3) \times 6^2 =$ _____

2) $23.8 \times 0.39 =$ _____

3) Kiran ran the 100m in **13.11** seconds and Krashna ran it in **12.87** seconds. How many seconds faster was Krashna? _____

4) Complete this number sequence:

$1\frac{3}{4}, \quad 2\frac{1}{2}, \quad 3\frac{1}{4}, \quad$ _____

5) $x = 9 \quad y = 7 \quad z = 2$

$\dfrac{x + y}{z} =$ _____

6) What is the highest common factor of **42**, **63** and **84**? _____

7) What is the next number?

0.0017, 0.017, 0.17, _____

8) Find the size of angle **Z**. _____

9) $8^4 =$ _____

10) Simon is the middle person in a row of students. He is also **19th** from the end. How many students are there in the whole row? _____

11) Sweets are shared in the ratio **7:4** between Randip and Roberta. Roberta receives the smaller share of **16**.
a) How many sweets does Randip receive? _____
b) How many sweets are there altogether? _____

12) Find the sum of the prime numbers between **46** and **66**. _____

13) $9^4 =$ _____

14) A local theatre has **6** seats in each of the **4** boxes, **21** rows of **25** seats in the circle and **16** rows of **12** seats in the stalls. How many seats are there altogether? _____

15) What is this quadrilateral called?

_____

Score

Percentage %

Do your workings on this page

© 2008 Stephen Curran ae

Mark to %	
0	0%
1	7%
2	13%
3	20%
4	27%
5	33%
6	40%
7	47%
8	53%
9	60%
10	67%
11	73%
12	80%
13	87%
14	93%
15	100%

Maths Test 35

1) $15.31 \div 1.6 =$ _____

Give your answer to **2 d.p.**

2) $10 \times$ _____ $\times 4 = 560$

3) What is the lowest common multiple of **6**, **9** and **14**? _____

4) What number is halfway between **-12** and **+6**? _____

5) What do the angles **A** and **B** add up to in this isosceles trapezium? _____

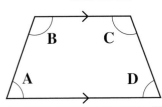

6) What is the highest common factor of **54**, **72** and **108**? _____

7) $\dfrac{2}{3} + \dfrac{4}{9} =$ _____

8) A clock chimes **6** times in **30** minutes. How many times does it chime in one day? _____

9) How does the time **7** minutes after midnight appear on a 24-hour clock? _____

10) Subtract the sum of the prime numbers between **92** and **102** from **250**. _____

11) What is the product of the even numbers between **17** and **23**? _____

12) **-8**, ____, **-1, 1, 2**

What is the missing number?

13) $1.1^3 =$ _____

14) The average amount of money spent by **5** girls on a shopping trip was **£26**. If the average amount spent by **4** of the girls was **£21**, how much did the **fifth** girl spend? _____

15) 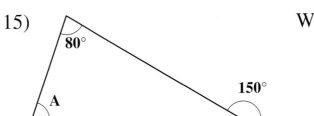 What is size of angle **A**? _____

Score ☐ **Percentage** ☐ **%**

Do your workings on this page

Mark to %	
0	0%
1	7%
2	13%
3	20%
4	27%
5	33%
6	40%
7	47%
8	53%
9	60%
10	67%
11	73%
12	80%
13	87%
14	93%
15	100%

Maths Test 36

1) What is the next number?

   4, 1, $\frac{1}{4}$, $\frac{1}{16}$, _____

2) $x = 2$ $y = 8$

   What is the value of:

   $y^2 \div x$? _____

3) On a plan a school classroom measures **7cm** by **9cm**. If the actual width of the classroom measures **10.5m**, what is the actual length of the classroom? _____

4) 2^5 is a prime factor of **96**. What is the other prime factor? _____

5) Susan wrote the answer to a mathematics question as **1.55** instead of the correct answer of **15.5**. What was the difference between Susan's answer and the correct answer? _____

6) What is the HCF of **28, 42** and **56**? _____

7) Complete this number sequence:

   4, 5, 9, 14, 23, 37, _____ , _____

8) $6^3 + 3^4 + 15^2 =$ _____

9) **46.1 ÷ 0.12 =** _____

   Give your answer to **2 d.p.**

10) What is **nine** minutes before midnight on the 24-hour clock? _____

11) Find the size of angle **A**.

   _____

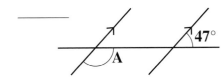

12) How many matches will there be altogether between **four** tennis players if they all play each other once? _____

13) Which shape has the most edges?

   _____

   A   **B**   **C**

14) What is the size of angle **A**?

   _____

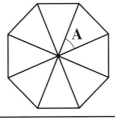

15)

A		
B		12
16	22	25

What are the values of **A** and **B**?

A = _____

B = _____

Score [ ]   Percentage [ ] %

Do your workings on this page

Mark to %	
0	0%
1	7%
2	13%
3	20%
4	27%
5	33%
6	40%
7	47%
8	53%
9	60%
10	67%
11	73%
12	80%
13	87%
14	93%
15	100%

Maths Test 37

1) Which is the odd one out?
   pyramid, triangular prism, trapezium, cone? _____

---

2) Write **10.41pm** as a time on a 24-hour clock. _____

3) $2^7 = 2 \times 2 \times 2 \times 2 \times 2 \times 2 \times 2 = 128$
   $3^7 =$ _____

---

4) In a theatre, rows of seats are lettered from **A** to **Z**. If there are **30** seats in each row, how many seats are there altogether? _____

---

5) The area of a tennis court is **2808 ft²**. If the width of the court is **36 ft**, what is its length? _____

---

6) What is the highest common factor of **72, 120** and **144**?

   _____

7) Use the conversion graph to find the following distances:
   a) **25 miles** = _____ km
   b) **200km** = _____ miles

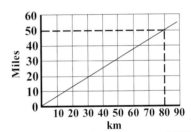

8) $4^3 + 5^2 + 1^5 =$ _____

9) What is the sum of the prime numbers between **72** and **90**?

   _____

---

10) When you turn a full circle you turn through **360°**. If you only turn **216°**, through what fraction of the circle have you turned? _____

---

11) What are the next two numbers in this sequence?

    19, 15, 10, 4, ____, ____

12) What is the volume of this cuboid?

    _____ 7cm 14cm 9cm

---

13) How many degrees are there in **6** right angles? _____

---

14) The sum of two numbers is **50**. Their difference is **8**. What are the two numbers? _____

---

15) What is the lowest common multiple of **3, 5** and **7**? _____

Score Percentage %

Do your workings on this page

Mark to %	
0	0%
1	7%
2	13%
3	20%
4	27%
5	33%
6	40%
7	47%
8	53%
9	60%
10	67%
11	73%
12	80%
13	87%
14	93%
15	100%

Maths Test 38

1) $0.47 \times 10^4 = $ _____

---

3) A woman is **28** years old. Her son is **one third** of her age. What age, in years and months, is her son?

_____

5) Complete this series:

3, 6, 18, 72, _____ , _____

7) The rows, columns and diagonals of this magic square add up to **108** in each direction. What are the values of **A** and **B**?

	B	32
20	36	
	A	

A = _____

B = _____

2) What is the area of this triangle? _____

Give your answer to the nearest whole number.

4.6cm
7.8cm

---

4) $1\frac{1}{14} \div \frac{6}{49} = $ _____

---

6) $\frac{n}{4} = 7$

What is the value of **n**? ____

---

8) What is the reflex angle made by the hands of this clock?

_____

---

9) Out of **120** children taking a science exam, **85%** passed. How many children did not pass? _____

---

10) When you square a certain number and then multiply the answer by **6** you get **54**. What is the number? _____

---

11) $\frac{3}{7}$ of the children in a sports club are boys. **52** are girls. How many children are there altogether in the club? _____

---

12) How many faces does a triangular based pyramid (tetrahedron) have? _____

13) $2\frac{4}{7} - 1\frac{3}{5} = $ _____

---

14) There are **five** basketball teams: A, B, C, D and E. How many games will be played, if every team plays each other once? _____

---

15) What is the order of rotational symmetry of this shape?

_____

Score ☐ Percentage ☐ %

Do your workings on this page

Mark to %	
0	0%
1	7%
2	13%
3	20%
4	27%
5	33%
6	40%
7	47%
8	53%
9	60%
10	67%
11	73%
12	80%
13	87%
14	93%
15	100%

Maths Test 39

1) What is the missing mixed number in this sequence?

2, $2\frac{1}{6}$, $2\frac{1}{3}$, _____ , $2\frac{2}{3}$

2)

$2\frac{5}{6} + 1\frac{9}{14} =$ _____

3) How many short of a million is **764,000**? _____

4) $\frac{5}{7}x = 15$

Find the value of x? _____

5) Peter scored **9** out of the **25** goals scored by his football team in a season. What % did the rest of the team score? _____

6) Find the value of z:

$5z + 17 = 38 - 2z$

$z =$ _____

7) What is the value of **A** in this magic square?

_____

	0.8	
A		
1.1	1.6	0.9

8) Write the ratio **42:28** in its lowest terms? _____

9) What is the perimeter of a square with an area of **81cm²**? _____

10) Add the sum of **11** and **12** to the product of **11** and **12** and the difference between **11** and **12**. _____

11) What is the smallest number that **4**, **6** and **7** will divide into, without leaving a remainder? _____

12) Calculate the following: _____ ⇢⟶ -6×13 ⟶ **221**

13) How many degrees is the anti-clockwise turn from southwest to north? _____

14) Water condenses at **32°F** and boils at **212°F**. What is the temperature difference between these values? _____

15)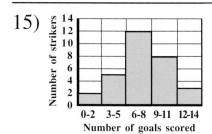

The bar chart shows the number of goals scored by **30** strikers in a 5-a-side football tournament. How many strikers scored:

a) between **6** and **11** goals? _____

b) **8** goals or less? _____

Score [ ] Percentage [ ] **%**

Do your workings on this page

Mark	to %
0	0%
1	7%
2	13%
3	20%
4	27%
5	33%
6	40%
7	47%
8	53%
9	60%
10	67%
11	73%
12	80%
13	87%
14	93%
15	100%

Maths Test 40

1) Complete this series:

    1, 10, 26, 51, _____

2) Find the value of *y*:

    6(3y – 2) = 114   *y* = ____

3) When **two** numbers are added together the total is **42**. The difference between the same **two** numbers is **12**. What are the numbers? _____

4) How many lines of symmetry does a rhombus have? _____

5) $1\frac{4}{17} \times 2\frac{3}{7} =$ ____

6) What is the area of this parallelogram? _____

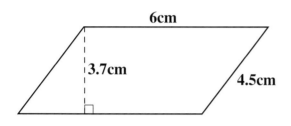

7) Find the height of this triangle.

_____

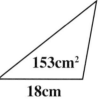

153cm²

18cm

8) **12 – (5 × 1.25) =** _____

9) ___ **÷ 1000 = 0.01**

10) A watch was put right at the **6pm** time signal. It lost **2** minutes every hour. What time did it show at the **6pm** time signal the next day? _____

11) **2, 5, 10, 7, 5, 9, 5, 9**

a) Range = ___   b) Mode = ___   c) Median = ___

12) $\dfrac{3.78}{1.4 \times 0.2} =$ ____

13) Plot the following coordinates and join them up. What shape does this give? _____

(1, 3) (3, 4) (5, 3) (3, 1)

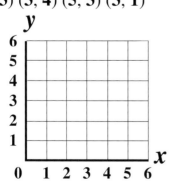

14) The area of the shaded triangle is **150mm²**. What is the area of the largest triangle?

_____ cm²

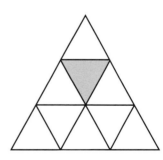

15) What is the size of angle **A**? _____

127°

136°

Score ☐   Percentage ☐ %

Notes

Answers

Test 1
1) 120
2) 13, 17
3) d
4) 6
5) 16
6) 6
7) 0.3
8) no
9) 100
10) $\frac{1}{100}$
11) 140
12) 180
13) 6
14) c
15) 168

Test 2
1) 5
2) 1.76
3) 920
4) 37
5) 10
6) vertical
7) 12
8) 55
9) 8
10) 4
11) a
12) c
13) 20 days and 6 hours
14) 1.75 or $1\frac{3}{4}$
15) 60

Test 3
1) 81
2) 1.5
3) 705
4) 1923
5) 22
6) $\frac{1}{4}$
7) 1, 2, 3, 4, 6, 8, 12, 24

8) 28
9) 3,600
10) 0.15 or $\frac{3}{20}$
11) 15
12) 24
13) 7.5
14) 8
15) Thursday

Test 4
1) 37
2) 0.35 or 35 hundredths
3) 31/12/2007
4) 5
5) 672
6) 10
7) 1, 2, 4, 7, 14, 28
8) 27
9) 1, 2, 3, 6
10) 21
11) reflex
12) 24
13) 99,995
14) c
15) d

Test 5
1) 4
2) yes
3) $\frac{1}{24}$
4) 1, 2, 3, 4, 6, 9, 12, 18, 36
5) 20
6) 360°
7) 24
8) 20
9) 105
10) 0.95
11) 135
12) Elaine
13) 3
14) 100
15) $\frac{1}{2}$

Test 6
1) 164
2) 19
3) Mandip
4) 0.9 or $\frac{9}{10}$ or 9 tenths
5) -6
6) 17
7) 36
8) 1,323
9) 10.73
10) 20
11) 4:3
12) 3:4
13) 3:7
14) 8.29am
15) F, H, T

Test 7
1) 0.45
2) 24
3) 1941
4) 6
5) 120°
6) 8
7) d
8) a
9) ⁙. or .⁙.
10) 5
11) 9.98
12) 3
13) 27p
14) 2:1
15) 44

Test 8
1) 89.243
2) 28
3) 42°
4) 6.6, $6\frac{1}{2}$, 6.45
5) 0.09 or $\frac{9}{100}$ or 9 hundredths
6) 341.6
7) 315

8) 87
9) 3:1
10) 3.16pm
11) 4:5
12) 92
13) 11.40pm
14) 4,170
15) 35

Test 9
1) 25 and 49
2) 3
3) 62
4) 34
5) $\frac{2}{3}$
6) 2
7) 13.775
8) 9
9) $\frac{52}{100}$, 1.52, $\frac{52}{10}$
10) 325°
11) $4\frac{1}{2}$, 4.1, 4.02
12) perpendicular
13) 9.06am
14) 7
15) 809

Test 10
1) 5.32
2) 48
3) 36
4) 4
5) 9
6) 12.5 or $12\frac{1}{2}$
7) 17.21
8) 672
9) 4:1
10) 396,000
11) 163
12) 21.5 or $21\frac{1}{2}$
13) 24
14) 4.5 hours or 4 hrs 30 mins or $4\frac{1}{2}$ hours
15) 8

Answers

Test 11
1) 2.9
2) 203
3) $\frac{1}{3}$
4) 185
5) 1, 17
6) $\frac{1}{6}$
7) 32
8) 28
9) 10 and 15
10) 13
11) 9
12) 4
13) 4
14) 0.04 or $\frac{4}{100}$ or 4 hundredths
15) 1

Test 12
1) 102
2) 0.494
3) 67
4) 1.7
5) 270°
6) 13
7) 85
8) 32
9) 485
10) yes
11) 40
12) false
13) 64
14) odd
15) 60

Test 13
1) ten thousand or 10,000
2) $\frac{1}{24}$
3) 18
4) $\frac{5}{12}$
5) 45
6) 8.25am

7) A
8) 2
9) 27
10) 448
11) 16
12) $\frac{52}{9}$
13) 2028
14) 0.3 or $\frac{3}{10}$ or 3 tenths
15) 3123

Test 14
1) 84.1
2) $2\frac{1}{2}$
3) 28
4) 1.3
5) 288°
6) 48
7) 7
8) 24
9) Sunday
10) –
11) 29
12) $\frac{1}{8}$
13) no
14) 4
15) 47 hours and 30 minutes

Test 15
1) £9.50
2) 48
3) east
4) 10
5) $1\frac{1}{3}$
6) 479.07
7) 8.10am
8) 400
9) $\frac{5}{6}$
10) 15 and 21
11) 11.1
12) 4
13) 20

14) $\frac{1}{6}$
15) 0.42

Test 16
1) $\frac{1}{625}$
2) 7
3) 60
4) 6 and 8
5) 7.8
6) 23
7) 7.8km
8) $1\frac{1}{2}$
9) 5
10) southeast
11) 99
12) 19th
13) £7.00
14) 25
15) August 1999

Test 17
1) 0.02
2) 16.2
3) 33
4) $2\frac{5}{16}$
5) 5.33pm
6) £15.00
7) 2,955
8) 115
9) $\frac{14}{25}$
10) A = 22, B = 14, C = 16
11) 72
12) $\frac{16}{4}$
13) 36 and 44
14) 640
15) circumference

Test 18
1) 13
2) $\frac{5}{18}$
3) $\frac{5}{8}$
4) northeast
5) $\frac{3}{8}$
6) 4

7) 10,000
8) 563.64
9) 65%
10) diameter
11) 3 and 9
12) 2
13) 82
14) $\frac{3}{8}$
15) 9.47am

Test 19
1) 233
2) 45%
3) 1
4) 30
5) 81, 144
6) 195.5
7) 4.03, 4.043, 4.3
8) 12
9) 53.174
10) B
11) 4.50pm
12) 54 and 108
13) 0.009
14) 360
15) Y = 21, Z = 18

Test 20
1) 919
2) $\frac{18}{25}$
3) 3.299, 3.3, 3.33
4) 42
5) 41%
6) A
7) 297
8) 180g
9) 196
10) 129.2
11) 32 and 40
12) 33
13) even
14) no
15) 365

Answers

Test 21
1) 18
2) 283
3) 17
4) 1
5) 2%
6) 16
7) 16, 32 and 48
8) square
9) 125
10) $1\frac{1}{4}$
11) 29
12) 9
13) 9%, $\frac{1}{12}$, 0.08
14) 159
15) Tuesday

Test 22
1) 7
2) 2
3) 27
4) 512
5) 207
6) £3
7) 82
8) 30°
9) Monday
10) 56
11) 130°
12) 400
13) 15
14) A = 10,
    B = 12, C = 2
15) 5 : 7

Test 23
1) 386
2) 980,000
3) 5
4) 0.5
5) 20
6) A = 14, B = 10
7) 3,996

8) 42
9) 25
10) 60%
11) 10°C
12) 90
13) 40%
14) 8
15) 65°

Test 24
1) 112%
2) 9%
3) 44
4) 3
5) 3,159
6) $\frac{3}{4}$
7) 80°
8) 250
9) 50°
10) 160°
11) 18 and 36
12) 70°
13) 0.36, $\frac{7}{20}$, 34.5%
14) 28
15) $\frac{5}{8}$

Test 25
1) 14
2) 15 days
3) 28 and 56
4) 233.18
5) 324
6) 0.06
7) 120
8) 12°C
9) 100°
10) 100
11) 255
12) 5
13) 3 in 13 or $\frac{3}{13}$
14) 83
15) Ranjeev

Test 26
1) 1,800,000
2) 144°
3) 33
4) 1,000
5) 166.89
6) 18
7) 96
8) 24
9) £4.14
10) 140
11) F, M, Z
12) 92
13) 3°C
14) 1,080
15) $\frac{5}{12}$

Test 27
1) 3.584
2) 227.5 or $227\frac{1}{2}$
3) 72
4) 615.4
5) 20
6) 35 minutes
7) 49
8) 36
9) 12
10) 40
11) 0
12) 33
13) 9
14) 23°
15) 7.5cm

Test 28
1) regular
   heptagon
2) 60%
3) 256
4) 10,000
5) 11
6) 30
7) 43°

8) 3.7
9) 28
10) 10
11) D
12) 7°C
13) 382
14) $\frac{1}{5}$
15) $\frac{3}{25}$

Test 29
1) 55°
2) 361
3) $\frac{1}{45}$
4) 680
5) regular
   octagon
6) 61°
7) 12
8) 23
9) 13
10) 40%
11) 169.22
12) 117°
13) 2,197
14) 125
15) 80%

Test 30
1) 25
2) 6
3) 60
4) 4
5) 15
6) -6, -5, -4
7) 22
8) 16
9) 120
10) D
11) 16 and 25
12) 162.1
13) $\frac{3}{32}$
14) £7.20
15) 55°

Answers

Test 31
1) 3.5
2) $\frac{3}{4}$
3) 63
4) 282.22
5) A=29, B=28
6) 71°
7) $\frac{1}{13}$, 13%, $\frac{31}{100}$
8) 16
9) 56
10) 7,110
11) 14
12) -12, -2, -1, 0, 1, 2, 5
13) 108°
14) 3.05am
15) $\frac{1}{5}$

Test 32
1) 6
2) 35
3) 18.25
4) no
5) 16
6) 7 years
7) 12
8) $\frac{1}{5}$ or 0.2
9) 6
10) $\frac{1}{12}$
11) 0.04
12) 84
13) 19:20
14) 559.3
15) 70°

Test 33
1) 3,600
2) 42
3) 13
4) 11
5) 1 or +1
6) 00:39
7) $\frac{3}{5}$
8) 2.25
9) 26
10) 64%
11) 106
12) 37
13) 118.14
14) 10.08pm
15) 29°

Test 34
1) 6,372
2) 9.282
3) 0.24 seconds
4) 4
5) 8
6) 21
7) 1.7
8) 104°
9) 4,096
10) 37
11) a) 28 b) 44
12) 220
13) 6,561
14) 741
15) trapezium

Test 35
1) 9.57
2) 14
3) 126
4) -3
5) 180°
6) 18
7) $1\frac{1}{9}$
8) 288
9) 00:07
10) 52
11) 7,920
12) -4
13) 1.331
14) £46
15) 70°

Test 36
1) $\frac{1}{64}$
2) 32
3) 13.5m
4) 3
5) 13.95
6) 14
7) 60, 97
8) 522
9) 384.17
10) 23:51
11) 133°
12) 6
13) C
14) 45°
15) A = 17, B = 30

Test 37
1) trapezium
2) 22:41
3) 2,187
4) 780
5) 78 ft
6) 24
7) a) 40km
   b) 125 miles
8) 90
9) 324
10) $\frac{3}{5}$
11) -3, -11
12) 882cm^3
13) 540°
14) 21 and 29
15) 105

Test 38
1) 4,700
2) 18cm^2
3) 9 years and 4 months
4) $8\frac{3}{4}$
5) 360, 2,160
6) 28
7) A = 44, B = 28
8) 240°
9) 18
10) 3
11) 91
12) 4
13) $\frac{34}{35}$
14) 10
15) 9

Test 39
1) $2\frac{1}{2}$
2) $4\frac{10}{21}$
3) 236,000
4) 21
5) 64%
6) 3
7) 1.0 or 1
8) 3:2
9) 36cm
10) 156
11) 84
12) 23
13) 225°
14) 180°F
15) a) 20 b) 19

Test 40
1) 87
2) 7
3) 15 and 27
4) 2
5) 3
6) 22.2cm^2
7) 17cm
8) 5.75
9) 10
10) 5.12pm
11) a) 8 b) 5 c) 6
12) 13.5 or $13\frac{1}{2}$
13) kite
14) 13.5cm^2
15) 83°

PROGRESS CHARTS

Test	Mark	%
1		
2		
3		
4		
5		
6		
7		
8		
9		
10		
11		
12		
13		
14		
15		
16		
17		
18		
19		
20		

Test	Mark	%
21		
22		
23		
24		
25		
26		
27		
28		
29		
30		
31		
32		
33		
34		
35		
36		
37		
38		
39		
40		

CERTIFICATE
OF
ACHIEVEMENT
(First)

This certifies ....
has completed **Maths Testbook One**
successfully.

Overall Percentage
Score Achieved.

%

Comment ....
....

Signed ....
(teacher/parent/guardian)

Date ....